CLEMSON

DABO'S
ALL IN TEAM™
FOUNDATION

500

Memorable Football
Trivia Q & A

by Mike McGuire

CLEMSON

DABO'S
ALL IN TEAM™
FOUNDATION

500

Memorable Football Trivia Q & A

by Mike McGuire

0-9772661-9-2

FIRST EDITION

Member of
The National Football Foundation & College Football Hall of Fame
Football Writers Association
Intercollegiate Football Research Association

Order copies from
Mike McGuire
555 Lesesne Street
Daniel Island, SC 29492-7460

mmcguire@mcguireusa.com
602.793.2383

Printed in the United States of America

PREFACE

Clemson ALL IN TEAM™ 500 Memorable Football Trivia Q & A was a lot of fun to write because of the tremendous amount of material available about the history, the tradition, and the competitive spirit of athletic competition of the Clemson football team. However, more important to me as the author is the association with the All in Team™ Foundation and that the net proceeds will be donated to the Foundation to support activities for Breast Cancer Research. I am an ardent supporter of "Paying it Forward" and believe this trivia book will assist in the fight against Cancer.

The 500 trivia questions and answers cover the players, the coaches, the stadium, key plays, the band, the bowl games, the fans, and some fun "nickel trivia facts." My trivia questions are meant to be tricky, thought-provoking, and confusing—to bring back good ole' memories while evaluating your knowledge of this, one of the greatest college football programs in America today. Laugh, cry, argue—but most of all, have fun with the trivia.

Another feature is the "Game Day WEATHER Forecast" that gives the GPS coordinates at the 50-yard line in Death Valley. The forecast will provide accurate information to help you determine how to dress for the game.

The list of National College Football Awards from different organizations will be interesting when Clemson players are in the running to win an award. Keep track of the Tiger winners.

"Clemson Football Books" section is an extensive list of books written all about the history of Clemson football, the coaches, the players, and National Championship seasons. The book list is current titles and what I call collectable antique books. Ebay and the website BookFinder are excellent sources for finding that special copy. Also order the *Annual Clemson Football Media Guide* for up-to-date information heading into the season.

Go Tigers!

Mike McGuire

HOW TO USE CLEMSON ALL IN TEAM™
500 MEMORABLE FOOTBALL TRIVIA Q & A

Trivia questions are always meant to be fun, tricky, thought provoking, confusing and to bring back good ole' memories, while testing one's knowledge of a particular subject. We do offer the following suggestions on "How to Use" the *Clemson ALL IN TEAM™ 500 Memorable Football Trivia Q & A* book for greater enjoyment.

It is great to use as a "Party Starter" for any Clemson Tiger fans gathering before kick-off and an excellent way to meet new people while also learning about the great traditions and history of Clemson Football. The book is laid out in a format of 20 questions and answers and Tiger fans can go along at their own pace. Each correct answer could be worth 5 points within a group of questions and individuals or teams awarded prizes for their skill and knowledge of Clemson ALL IN TEAM™ Memorable Football Trivia.

Tailgating...a great way to pass the time as the hamburgers and hotdogs are cooking on the grill. Play to see who cooks or who cleans up after the meal!

On the Road...driving to and from a Clemson game, trivia can help make the miles pass faster. Play to see who drives and who asks the questions, or who buys the next tank of gas, food, or cocktails.

On an Airplane, Bus, or Train...a great way to study and improve your knowledge of Clemson Football traditions, history, records, players, coaches and more. Upon your arrival impress your friends with your Clemson football trivia knowledge. Maybe even meet other Clemson Tiger fans traveling with you.

Local Pub or Pizza Joint...A pizza and beer always taste better with great sports trivia conversations, discussions and arguments and it doesn't get any better than Clemson Football.

First Date at Clemson...Not highly recommended unless there is prior knowledge of the other person's love for Clemson Football.

In the Bathroom...OK! But please keep the book on your nightstand or a bookshelf.

Send me the unique ways on how you have used the *Clemson ALL IN TEAM™ 500 Memorable Football Trivia Q & A* to **mmcguire@mcguireusa.com**.

TABLE OF CONTENTS

GROUP 1 QUESTIONS

1-1 Which four Clemson Head Football Coaches are in the College Football Hall of Fame?

1-2 Through 2024, How many Head Football Coaches have coached at Clemson?

1-3 Who tagged Clemson's Memorial Stadium as "Death Valley"?

1-4 Which Head Coach had a winning percentage of .833, best in Clemson history?

1-5 What year did Clemson join the Atlantic Coast Conference (ACC)?

1-6 What year was the "Tiger Paw" Introduced?

1-7 **T or F:** The 2018 National Champions won their final 10 games by 20+ points.

1-8 How many seasons was Dabo Swinney an Assistant Coach at Clemson?

1-9 How many 100+ yard rushing games did Travis Etienne have in his career?

1-10 Which two linebackers lead the team in tackles for three seasons each?

1-11 What is "The most exciting 25 seconds in college football?

1-12 Who did Clemson play in its very first football game?

1-13 Which team had a perfect season with four shutouts and outscored its opponents 222-10?

1-14 Where does Clemson rank in size of football stadiums?

1-15 What was the first victory in Clemson football history over a Top 20 ranked team?

1-16 Who was the first ACC player in history to earn first team all-conference honors at three distinct positions (running-back, all-purpose and specialist)?

1-17 **T or F:** Brothers William Perry and Michael Perry are both on the ACC 50 Year Anniversary team.

1-18 Who holds the record for consecutive 100+ yard rushing games?

1-19 Who was the first Tiger football player to have his jersey number retired?

1-20 What year did the IPTAY Scholarship Club start?

GROUP 1 ANSWERS

1-1   John Heisman, Jess Neely, Frank Howard, Danny Ford

1-2   25

1-3   Presbyterian College Head Coach Lonnie McMillian during the 1940s.

1-4   John Heisman, 19-3-2 in only four years

1-5   1953 The year before playing as an Independent

1-6   July 21, 1970

1-7   True!

1-8   6 Seasons, 2003-2008

1-9   20, best game 212 yards against Wofford 2019

1-10   Tim Jones, 92-94, Anthony Simmons, 95-97

1-11   Per Sportscaster Brent Musburger, "Running Down the Hill"

1-12   At Furman, October 31, 1896

1-13   1900

1-14   12th, 81,500, BUT the largest in the ACC; Top three largest stadiums are all in the Big Ten: Michigan 107,601, Penn State 106,572, and THE Ohio State "Horseshoe" 102,780.

1-15   6-3 over Boston College, 1940 Cotton Bowl, Head Coach Jess Neely

1-16   2022 Will Shipley

1-17   True!

1-18   Six in a row! Travis Etienne, 2019

1-19   QB Steve Fuller #4, also a member of the Clemson Ring of Honor

1-20   1934

GROUP 2 QUESTIONS

2-1   December 2021, who is the latest Clemson player to be inducted into the College Football Hall of Fame?

2-2   The faded Navy color of the original jersey became purplish in color, officially, known today as _____?

2-3   Through 2023, How many consecutive bowl games (seasons) has Clemson played?

2-4   Who coached the team for FREE as Clemson had no money to pay a coach?

2-5   Who was the first QB in Division 1 to reach 2,000 yards passing and 1,00 yards rushing in a single season?

2-6   Which season was Clemson the only Division 1 school to have two returning Academic All-Americans?

2-7   Which season did Jeff Davis win an ACC MVP, lead the league in tackles (175), was first-time All-American, by UPI, Kodak, Football writers and Football News?

2-8   Head Coach Dabo Swinney is currently second in the number of wins as a member of the ACC. Who is first?

2-9   Who has had the most rushing carries in his Clemson career?

2-10 What is Dabo Swinney's pet Goldendoodle's name?

2-11 Which coach has had the longest career at Clemson, and eight conference championships?

2-12 Which QB had three consecutive 300+ yard passing games?

2-13 Which season did Clemson first become ranked in the Top 20 in the AP Final Poll?

2-14 How many years had South Carolina played before Clemson started in 1896?

2-15 Which team did Clemson have three touchdown plays of at least 76 yards, yet lost the game?

2-16 Which two teams from 2015 to 2022 had 100 wins or more?

2-17 Which Clemson player led the NFL in the Stat Category of Receptions?

2-18 What year was Clemson's entire starting defensive line drafted in the first four rounds?

2-19 Through 2023, how many nine-win seasons did Head Coach Dabo Swinney produce?

2-20 Name the five Clemson Head Coaches who played at Alabama.

GROUP 2 ANSWERS

2-1   C.J. Spiller

2-2   Regalia

2-3   19, since 2005

2-4   Walter Riggs, 1899

2-5   QB Woodrow Dantzler, 2001

2-6   2000, Chad Carson and Kyle Young

2-7   National Championship Team, 1981, Perfect record 12-0

2-8   Bobby Bowden FSU, 173 wins, Dabo Swinney should pass him by season 2024.

2-9   805, Raymond Priester, 1994-97; 12 consecutive carries vs. Maryland 1997

2-10 LEVI. Named after the stadium where Dabo Swinney won his National Championship in January 2019

2-11 Frank Howard, 30 years, 1940-1969, Clemson's 17th Head Coach

2-12 Tajh Boyd 2013, he did it twice that year!

2-13 1939, 9-1-0 and beat Boston College #11 6-3 in the Cotton Bowl for its first win over a Top 20 Team

2-14 Five years and played every year in Columbia through 1959 and referred to as the "Big Thursday" Game

2-15 South Carolina, 2006

2-16 Alabama 103, Clemson 100

2-17 Dwight Clark, 60 receptions, 15.2 yards per catch, 1982

2-18 2018

2-19 13

2-20 Swinney, Howard, Ford, Pell, Ingram

 GROUP **3** QUESTIONS

3-1   Who holds the ACC record for career All-Purpose Yardage?

3-2   **T or F:** Clemson has had two consecutive undefeated seasons.

3-3   What conference did Clemson play in at the beginning?

3-4   How is the "Tiger Paw" properly displayed?

3-5   Which Clemson Coaches played for future Clemson coach John Heisman?

3-6   Which game did Clemson set the record of 756 yards of total offense, 536 yards rushing?

3-7   **T or F:** Through 2022, Clemson had 12 consecutive seasons with 10 or more wins.

3-8   As of 2023, name the three running backs who became consensus All-Americans at Clemson.

3-9   How many consecutive years did Clemson have a wideout selected in the NFL Draft?

3-10   Who was the position coach at Alabama for Dabo and later hired him at Clemson in 2003?

3-11   Where did Clemson play its first game inside a dome stadium?

3-12   In 2009, who was the only player in the nation to score at least one touchdown in every game?

3-13   Coach Pell left Clemson after two years to coach which team in 1978?

3-14   What Rivalry Game was held on Thursdays to commemorate state fair week in Columbia?

3-15   Which Big Ten team has three markers in the Clemson "Graveyard" as a ranked team and an away game for Clemson?

3-16   Which season for the first time was Clemson ranked in the final AP Poll (12th) and beat a Top 20 team?

3-17   Which former All-American Clemson player was the first player in NFL history to register a sack, an interception, recover a fumble and score a touchdown in the same game?

3-18   **T or F:** Clemson has been in the Top 20 in the country for average home attendance for 44 straight years.

3-19   What book did Tim Bourret write that tells The Story of the Tigers?

3-20   Who is considered Clemson's football founding father?

 GROUP **3** ANSWERS

3-1   C.J. Spiller, 7,588 yards

3-2   True! 2018, 2019, two consecutive regular seasons

3-3   Southern Intercollegiate Athletic Association (SIAA)

3-4   Turned to the 1:00 Angle; Coach Frank Howard said, "All football games should start at 1:00."

3-5   W.M Williams at Auburn 1894-95-96 and John Penton 1897

3-6   1981, vs. Wake Forest 82-24 on Halloween

3-7   True!

3-8   C.J. Spiller, Travis Etienne, Terrence Flagler

3-9   Six Years, 2016-2021

3-10   Coach Tommy Bowden

3-11   Superdome vs. Tulane 1981, winning 13-5.

3-12   C.J. Spiller, 14 games

3-13   University of Florida

3-14   "Big Thursday" South Carolina & Clemson. Frank Howard never liked this arrangement.

3-15   THE Ohio State Buckeyes, #7 (1-13-14 40-35), #2 (12-31-16 31-0) and #2 (12-28-19 29-23).

3-16   1939

3-17   Pro Football Hall of Fame 2018 Inductee Brian Dawkins

3-18   True!

3-19   *Clemson Football Vault*. The book all Tiger Fans should have on their bookshelf.

3-20   Walter Merritt Riggs, 1896 (2-1)

GROUP 4 QUESTIONS

4-1   Which team is Clemson's biggest rival?

4-2   Why is Clemson called the Tigers?

4-3   **T or F:** Clemson was unranked in every preseason poll in 1981.

4-4   Coach John Heisman first year 1900, he went 6-0; how many games did he shut-out the opponent?

4-5   Who was the first coach in college history to win a bowl game in his first game without having coached the team in any capacity earlier in the year?

4-6   **T or F:** Clemson was the only school to have six defensive players drafted in 1999.

4-7   Which former coach at Clemson won 33 straight games later in his career?

4-8   Who was Clemson's first All-American in any sport?

4-9   Which four football individuals were Charter Members of the Clemson Hall of Fame?

4-10   Dabo Swinney was a full-time Assistant Coach at Alabama in 1996 under which Legendary Head Coach?

4-11   How many shutouts has Clemson had in a season?

4-12   Who holds the record for total offensive yards in a single game by Clemson?

4-13   How many times did Coach Danny Ford have Clemson rated #1 in the Final AP and Coaches Poll?

4-14   Who stated, "If Banks McFadden drank a can of tomato juice, they could have used him as a thermometer."

4-15   Who is the only (so far) former Tiger to win the NFL MVP Honor?

4-16   What is the "Dabo Tron?"

4-17   When was the first time Clemson had a 100-yard rusher, 200-yard passer and a 100-yard receiver in the same game?

4-18   Which season did Clemson have its highest final ranking at the time as Number Six?

4-19   Who set the NCAA record for single game kick-off return yardage?

4-20   Which All-American ended his career with four game-winning field goals?

GROUP 4 ANSWERS

Clemson Football Trivia

Answers

4-1　South Carolina Gamecocks, an In-State Rivalry

4-2　The first head coach came from Auburn, and the Princeton (Tigers) had won the National Championship in 1895

4-3　True!

4-4　Four times, first undefeated season!

4-5　Tommy West, 1993 Peach Bowl win over Kentucky 14-13

4-6　True!

4-7　John Heisman, 1904-1919 at Georgia Tech

4-8　O.K. Pressley, 1928; LB and Center as players played both ways at this time.

4-9　Coach Frank Howard, Players Joe Blalock, Fred Cone, Banks McFadden

4-10　Gene Stallings

4-11　7 in 1928, 6 of them consecutive!

4-12　588 yards by Deshaun Watson vs. Pittsburgh, but lost the game 42-43 (2016)

4-13　One time, 1981, National Championship year. Coach Dabo Swinney through 2023 did it twice in 2016 and 2018.

4-14　Coach Frank Howard, a typical "Lite Moment," Banks McFadden was 6'-3", 165 pounds.

4-15　Dwight Clark #87, 1982 as a San Francisco 49er'

4-16　Video Board, 126' wide, 56.5' tall

4-17　1947 vs. Auburn! A "J S" (Job Saver) game for Coach Frank Howard

4-18　1978, after a Gator Bowl 17-15 win over THE Ohio State Buckeyes in Danny Ford's first game as Head Coach.

4-19　Justin Miller (2004) vs. Florida State, 282 yards and two touchdowns

4-20　David Treadwell (1985-1987)

GROUP 5 QUESTIONS

5-1   Which Clemson running back set a Tigers' scoring record with 108 points in 2000?

5-2   When was the first meeting between the Clemson Tigers and the South Carolina Gamecocks?

5-3   Who was the first Clemson player drafted No. 1 overall in the NFL?

5-4   **T or F:** Clemson finished with a 15-0 record against a schedule that included 12 teams with a winning record in 2018.

5-5   After the 2023 Bowl Season, what was Clemson's record all time in bowl games?

5-6   Which coach seconded his own nomination to become Head Coach at a meeting with the Clemson President and Athletic Council?

5-7   **T or F:** Football derives its existence from the English game of soccer.

5-8   Which Clemson coach was a member of the "Football Trinity?"

5-9   Who was known as the "Little Giant" of the Crimson Tides "Herd of Red Elephants?"

5-10   What was the longest run Trevor Lawrence had at Clemson?

5-11   What was the reason Head Coach Charley Pell resigned from Clemson to coach Florida?

5-12   **T or F:** Clemson won five straight bowl games between 1986-1990.

5-13   Who was the Head Coach (30 years old) who in his first game defeated which college football legend?

5-14   What season did Clemson reach 28,000+ plus points scored in its history?

5-15   **T or F:** The 1981 National Championship Clemson team the first ACC team to win a National Championship in football.

5-16   Who is the leading Defensive Back tackler in Clemson history?

5-17   Which season did Clemson rank in the Top 25 in punting, place kicking, punt returns, and kickoff returns?

5-18   Who was the first Clemson Head Coach to win 10 games in his first season?

5-19   How many Conference Titles did Head Coach John Heisman win outright?

5-20   Which two former Clemson players played for 16 seasons games in the NFL?

GROUP 5 ANSWERS

5-1   Travis Zachery

5-2   November 12, 1896, South Carolina winning 12-6.

5-3   QB Trevor Lawrence, by the Jacksonville Jaguars

5-4   True!

5-5   27-22

5-6   Frank Howard, 1940

5-7   False! Rugby was the game!

5-8   1920s, John Heisman, along with Alonzo Stagg and Pop Warner

5-9   Coach Frank Howard

5-10   67 yards vs. THE Ohio State Buckeyes and it broke their back!

5-11   He did not think Clemson would ever win a National Championship.

5-12   True!

5-13   Danny Ford, 1978 Gator Bowl 17-15, beating THE Ohio State Buckeyes legendary coach Woody Hayes, his last game.

5-14   In 2021, 28,086 points. 1896 to 2021, 125 years

5-15   False, Maryland won one in 1953, its first year in the ACC.

5-16   Career 374, Robert Carswell's title still holds.

5-17   1995, Coach Tommy West, only Clemson team to ever achieve this record.

5-18   Coach Ken Hatfield, 1990, Ranking #9 in the AP Poll

5-19   2, 1900, 1902, Southern Intercollegiate Athletic Association (SIAA)

5-20   Chris Gardocki and Brian Dawkins

 GROUP 6 QUESTIONS

6-1 Through 2022, how many Conference Championships does Clemson hold?

6-2 Which game did Clemson force nine turnovers during the 1981 championship season?

6-3 From 2018-2020, Clemson accounted for how many of the most-watched college football games and how many of the 10 most-watched games?

6-4 Who did Clemson play to win its very first bowl game?

6-5 **T or F:** Clemson was the first school to play in two bowl games in the same calendar year.

6-6 Which season did Clemson first beat three Top 10 Teams?

6-7 What is the Long Lat at center field (50 Yard Line) at Clemson's Memorial Stadium?

6-8 Which team bet Clemson they would give them a bushel of apples for every point above their margin to defeat Georgia Tech?

6-9 Who holds the record for the longest Clemson punt?

6-10 Which former Clemson player lead the NFL in Net Punting in 2000?

6-11 Which team snapped Clemson's 40 home game winning streak?

6-12 What was the first Clemson win over a Big Ten team?

6-13 What does IPTAY stand for?

6-14 How long is the current record for consecutive home wins at Memorial Stadium?

6-15 How many conference titles did Head Coach Frank Howard win at Clemson?

6-16 How many seasons has Clemson had a 100% winning percentage through 2023?

6-17 Which National Championship team won eight away games?

6-18 How many games in a four-game series with Alabama's Bear Bryant did Head Coach Frank Howard win?

6-19 Which game was the first "Puntrooskie" trick played to a surprised crowd?

6-20 Who holds the record for punting average for a season (44.5 yards) and career (43.5 yards) as of 2023?

GROUP 6 ANSWERS

6-1 27

6-2 Georgia

6-3 Four most watched, five of the Top 10 most watched

6-4 Boston College, 6-3 win, 1940 Cotton Bowl

6-5 True! 1959 Sugar Bowl and 1959 First Bluebonnet Bowl in December

6-6 1981 National Championship season 12-0

6-7 34 Degrees, 40 Minutes, 43 Seconds Longitude
     82 Degrees, 50 Minutes, 36 Seconds Latitude

6-8 Clemson won the bet! Beat Tech 73-0 or 44 more points than they beat
     Georgia 10/10/1903.

6-9 Mitch Tyner, 81 yards vs. Texas A & M, 1973

6-10 Chris Gardocki, Cleveland Browns

6-11 South Carolina, 2022, 31-30

6-12 1978 Gator Bowl win over THE Ohio State Buckeyes, 17-15

6-13 "I Pay Ten a Year" to support Student-Athletes

6-14 40, began with a 56-7 win over South Carolina 2017 and was ended by
      South Carolina 31-30, 2022.

6-15 8 in total, 2 Southern Conference, 6 ACC

6-16 Four Seasons: 1900, 1948, 1981, 2018

6-17 2016

6-18 Zero (0-4)

6-19 Florida State University, 1988, winning 24-21.

6-20 Chris Gardocki, 1988-1990

 GROUP 7 QUESTIONS

7-1 Who led the NFL one season in passing yards (4,833), passing yards/attempt (8.9), yards /completion (12.6) and total offense (5,267) yards?

7-2 Who led Clemson in tackles for loss (LTF) for three seasons?

7-3 What is the greatest number of points Clemson has scored in a game?

7-4 Clemson played how many football teams from North Carolina in 2002?

7-5 Which colleges played in the first college football game?

7-6 Which Clemson Head Coach was on the 1961 National Championship team at Alabama?

7-7 Clemson crushed which in-state football rival 63-17 in 2003?

7-8 Who is the only Clemson graduate to serve as Head Coach of the Tigers?

7-9 Clemson and what football team participated in a massive brawl during a 2004 game?

7-10 What are the most home game wins Clemson has had over the years?

7-11 What is the record for consecutive extra points made?

7-12 Which Heisman Trophy winner threw the winning touchdown pass to beat Clemson 7-0 in the Sugar Bowl?

7-13 What game did Head Coach Dabo Swinney win his 100th ACC game?

7-14 Which Clemson Defensive Player holds the career record for Tackles for Loss?

7-15 Which Clemson player had 69 starts (12 more than any other Tiger) in history?

7-16 From 1940 to 2023, how many first round NFL draft picks has Clemson had?

7-17 Which Head Coach was respected for his integrity and loyalty as written by columnist Dan Foster of the *Greenville News?*

7-18 How many coaches who are inducted into the College Football Hall of Fame did Head Coach Danny Ford beat by 2018?

7-19 Which Clemson kicker held 14 school records, 25 multiple field goal games and three games with five field goals?

7-20 Through the 2023 season, what is Clemson's 128-year over-all record?

GROUP 7 ANSWERS

7-1   Deshaun Watson, 2020, Texans

7-2   Randy Scott 1976 (12), –77 (18), –78 (11)

7-3   122 vs, Guilford, 1901, Coach John Heisman

7-4   Four: Wake Forest, NC State, Duke, North Carolina

7-5   Princeton vs. Rutgers, November 6, 1869, New Brunswick, NJ

7-6   Charley Pell, Head Coach 1977-1978

7-7   South Carolina Gamecocks

7-8   Coach Shack Shealy

7-9   South Carolina Gamecocks

7-10   7: 1987, 2011, 2014, 2015, 2017, 2018, 2019, Road Wins many times, 2019 Last Time

7-11   122 by B.T. Potter 2018-20

7-12   Billy Cannon (LSU), 1959 Sugar Bowl

7-13   Syracuse, September 30, 2023, 31-14

7-14   Michael Dean Perry, 61, 1984-87

7-15   Will Spiers

7-16   39

7-17   Head Coach Frank Howard

7-18   26 Woody Hayes being his first — 1978 Gator Bowl

7-19   Nelson Welch (1991-1994)

7-20   798-472-45 (.624%)

 GROUP 8 QUESTIONS

8-1 Who was the first Clemson player enshrined in the Pro Football Hall of Fame in Canton, Ohio, 2018?

8-2 Who was the first Clemson player to be inducted into the College Football Hall of Fame?

8-3 What five Clemson Head Coaches have won the ACC Coach of the Year Award?

8-4 Why was the game between Clemson and South Carolina suspended for seven seasons?

8-5 What year was Clemson home to the NFL's Carolina Panthers?

8-6 Which season would Clemson only score three touchdowns and win just one game?

8-7 What two seasons was a future Head Coach at West Virginia, Michigan, and Arizona coach at Clemson as an Assistant Coach?

8-8 Awards named after two Legendary Head Football Coaches were won by Dabo in 2018, name the two coaches.

8-9 Who are the only two former Clemson players to score multiple rushing TDs, multiple receiving TDs, and multiple kick return TDs during their NFL careers?

8-10 What is Clemson's home winning percentage since 2014 through 2023, the CFP Era?

8-11 Which Clemson Quarterback has the record for consecutive pass completions?

8-12 What is the hottest temperature Clemson has played in at kickoff time?

8-13 Which Head Coach was raising tomatoes in Texas when he was approached to coach at Auburn before coming to Clemson?

8-14 Which ACC team through the 2023 season has won the most Conference Championships?

8-15 What is the worst score suffered by Ohio State fans vs. Clemson?

8-16 What was the first time Clemson beat South Carolina to claim the State Championship?

8-17 Who did Clemson beat in the Gator Bowl to go undefeated in 1948?

8-18 Frank Howard was the third Clemson Head Coach to be inducted into the College Football Hall of Fame. Who were the other two coaches that preceded Howard?

8-19 Who set the Clemson record with eight career kickoff returns for touchdowns?

8-20 Through 2023 Clemson has claimed 27 Conference Championships and 50 post season Bowl Games with an over-all record of what?

GROUP 8 ANSWERS

8-1   Brian Dawkins

8-2   Banks McFadden, 1959

8-3   Frank Howard, Charley Pell, Danny Ford, Tommy Bowden, and Dabo Swinney

8-4   A riot by fans from both South Carolina and Clemson, October 30, 1902

8-5   1995 the Panthers played at Death Valley, 1996 Panthers moved into their new stadium Bank of America in Charlotte, North Carolina

8-6   1931, but started the idea of IPTAY Foundation

8-7   Rich Rodriguez 1999-2000

8-8   Woody Hayes and Bear Bryant plus Dabo has won other National Coach-of-the-Year Awards.

8-9   Jacoby Ford and C.J. Spiller

8-10   95.6%, 65-3 tied with Alabama as Number 1

8-11   Deshaun Watson, 19 in 2016

8-12   95 degrees, twice 2004 and 2011

8-13   John Heisman, Clemson Head Coach, 1900-1903

8-14   Clemson 27, Duke 18, and Florida State 16

8-15   31-0, no touchdowns for the Buckeyes, Fiesta Bowl 2016

8-16   1897 (18-6 victory) by Coach W.M. Williams

8-17   Missouri (24-23), January 1, 1949

8-18   John Heisman and Jess Neely

8-19   C.J. Spiller

8-20   27-23

GROUP 9 QUESTIONS

9-1   Name the five Clemson players who earned All-American Honors in 1981.

9-2   **T or F:** Clemson is in the Top 10 Schools for winning Bowl Games.

9-3   Who was named first team All-American as a first-year student?

9-4   Who stated, "When in doubt, punt!?"

9-5   Which Head Coach never had a losing season overall or in the ACC with a 72-45 record?

9-6   "Running Down the Hill" is one of college football's most celebrated traditions. Which season did the tradition start?

9-7   **T or F:** Clemson has been ranked in the Final Top 10 from 2015 through 2022.

9-8   Which football team handed Clemson its first-ever loss in overtime in 2005?

9-9   Through the 2022 season, Clemson had a 40 game home winning streak. Who holds the longest home winning streak in FBS history at 58 wins?

9-10 The United Press (UPI) awarded Head Coach Danny Ford National Coach of the Week for the first time after beating whom?

9-11 Who is the leading career tackler at Clemson?

9-12 What was the first bowl game Clemson played in?

9-13 In the ACC, what is the "Clemson Rule?"

9-14 Which Clemson Head Coach improvised the use of a lateral and the center snap?

9-15 Through the 2024 NFL Draft, how many Clemson players have been drafted over the years?

9-16 **T or F:** In the Clemson vs. South Carolina series, the visiting team won seven consecutive games played between 1991-1997.

9-17 Who kicked six field goals for a total of 217 yards in a victory over Boston College 25-7?

9-18 Which Quarterback holds the record with 580 yards passing in a single game?

9-19 Which team did Clemson defeat to give Head Coach John Heisman a perfect record in 1900?

9-20 Which team had three 100-yard rushers in consecutive games?

 GROUP **9** ANSWERS

9-1   Bryant, Davis, Kinard, Nanney and Tuttle

9-2   True!

9-3   Sammy Watkins, 2011

9-4   Coach John Heisman

9-5   Tommy Bowden

9-6   1942

9-7   False! But ranked in the Top 15 each season.

9-8   Miami Hurricanes

9-9   Miami Hurricanes

9-10   Georgia, 1981, 13-3

9-11   Bubba Brown, 515, 1976-1979

9-12   1940 Cotton Bowl, Clemson Beating Boston College 6-3

9-13   An amendment (1982) to its 1978 Rule governing Crowd Noise. Two warnings in a game-violation resulted in a penalty on the home team.

9-14   Head Coach John Heisman, and he loved the forward pass!

9-15   293!

9-16   True!

9-17   Richard Jackson, 2009. Jad Dean also kicked six field goals in 2005.

9-18   Deshaun Watson vs. Pittsburgh, 2016

9-19   Alabama (35-0). Clemson's only perfect season during its first 52 years of football.

9-20   1950, runners Calvert, Mathews, and Cone with three straight shutouts along the way! 115-0. Great Offensive Line!

 # GROUP 10 QUESTIONS

10-1 Strength Coach George Dostal constructed a sign for offseason conditioning stating what?

10-2 Which two brothers were named ACC Player of the Year during their careers at Clemson?

10-3 Which two Clemson players were second in voting for two years each for the Rimington Trophy as best center in the country?

10-4 What is the winningest decade for Clemson?

10-5 Which two Clemson players have won the Archie Griffin Award as the Top Player in the Nation?

10-6 **T or F:** Head Coach John Heisman beat Ohio State twice and Michigan once in 1892 at Oberlin.

10-7 Who authored "The Clemson Tigers from 1896 to Glory?"

10-8 What year was Clemson Memorial Stadium built?

10-9 What was the game in which Clemson surrendered touchdowns on offense, defense, and special teams in a single game?

10-10 Which season was Clemson's first undefeated team?

10-11 Which ACC Head Coach would like to see no more rankings published on recruiting class, but rank each class four years later based on, on-field performance?

10-12 What was the "Baskin Robbins" game?

10-13 What ACC football team won in Memorial Stadium in 2002 for the first time since 1985?

10-14 In 1981, what team ended Clemson's streak of not allowing a touchdown in 18 straight quarters?

10-15 Since 2013, which team can claim the most wins against Power Five Conference opponents through 2022?

10-16 During construction of Memorial Stadium, which Head Coach placed a chew of tobacco in each of the four corners of the field when concrete was being poured?

10-17 How many 100-yard receiving games did Sammy Watson have setting the record?

10-18 What four Head Coaches considered by the College Football Hall of Fame were the expert innovators of college football?

10-19 Who was Clemson's last three-sport lettered athlete?

10-20 Which two Bowl Games did Clemson win where a safety occurred?

GROUP 10 ANSWERS

10-1 1982 Orange Bowl, Clemson vs. Nebraska

10-2 William Perry 1984, Michael Dean Perry 1987

10-3 Kyle Young (2000-2001), Dalton Freeman (2011-2012)

10-4 2010s 117-13-0 (83.6%), 30 more wins than any other decade.

10-5 Deshaun Watson 2015, Trevor Lawrence 2018

10-6 True! Ohio State 40-0 and 50-0; Michigan 24-22

10-7 Lou Sahadi, Sportswriter

10-8 1942

10-9 Notre Dame, November 5, 2020, 35-14 loss.

10-10 1900, Coached by John Heisman, 6-0

10-11 Dabo Swinney, and this author agrees 100%!

10-12 2016 Fiesta Bowl, Play-off game vs. THE Ohio State Buckeyes, 31-0

10-13 Maryland

10-14 Duke 1981, third quarter, Clemson winning 38-10.

10-15 Clemson with 102, followed by Alabama 99 and THE Ohio State University 94

10-16 Frank Howard

10-17 15

10-18 John Heisman, Amos Alonzo Stagg, Pop Warner, and Walter Camp

10-19 Frank Gillespie, guard on football team and basketball team and lettered in baseball. Won the 1947-48 McKelvin Award and inducted into the Clemson Athletic Hall of Fame 1977.

10-20 Orange Bowl 1951 vs. Miami 15-14, and 1949 Gator Bowl vs. Missouri 24-23.

GROUP 11 QUESTIONS

11-1 Who was the first unanimous first-team All-American in Clemson football history?

11-2 Someone once said that in the South, there are three seasons. Name them!

11-3 Which Head Coach coached in nine post-season all-star games?

11-4 What was the name of the first Clemson football field?

11-5 Who led the NCAA with 186 tackles and 35 tackles for loss in 1999?

11-6 Who did William "The Fridge" go against vs. Nebraska in the National Championship Game?

11-7 What is the only Big-Ten team played when Clemson has had over 500 yards in total offense?

11-8 With 100 wins at the end of 2022, Clemson was second to which team for the most wins since 2015?

11-9 Who was the first player in the history of the Walter Camp All-American Team to be a first or second team All-American at two positions in the same year?

11-10 Historically, what is the highest scoring quarter for Clemson?

11-11 Which Head Coach was on a National Championship team and led the country in punt returns twice?

11-12 What are the "Rally Cats?"

11-13 Clemson produced the ACC record for consecutive home wins from 2016-2022 with how many?

11-14 Which running back put back-to-back seasons rushing for over 1,600+ plus yards each year?

11-15 Which team did Clemson riot with when the Chief referee could not make the game due to a train accident?

11-16 Which two famous Hall of Fame coaches and close friends died on the same date 13 years apart?

11-17 What year was the Clemson Tiger Paw logo copyrighted?

11-18 Which Head Coach had the team enter the stadium from the West End Zone instead of "Running Down the Hill" except for his last game?

11-19 **T or F:** In 1981, Clemson was ranked by the Associated Press and all the football magazines in the Preseason Top 20.

11-20 Who is the outfitter for Clemson's uniforms?

 GROUP **11** ANSWERS

11-1 Terry Kinard, 1982

11-2 Football Season, Recruiting Season and Spring Practice

11-3 Frank Howard, Blue Gray (1941, 1952, 1959, 1966); East-West (1960, 1962); North-South (1961, 1969) and Hula Bowl (1970)

11-4 Bowman Field

11-5 All-American Keith Adams, PWS 16 sacks

11-6 Dave Rimington – The Greatest Center in College Football

11-7 THE Ohio State University, (2013) 576 yards! Also drove 99 yards to win 29-23, (2019).

11-8 Alabama, won 103, lost 10 vs. Clemson 100 wins, 13 losses. Winning percentage .912% to .885%

11-9 C.J. Spiller, 2009; also, sixth in Heisman, ACC Player of the Year and Unanimous First Team All American.

11-10 Second Quarter, and typically the same for Clemson's opponents.

11-11 Coach Ken Hatfield, 1963-1964 and second in 1962.

11-12 All-Girl Cheerleading Squad

11-13 40 game winning streak

11-14 Travis Etienne, 2018 (1,658 yards), 2019 (1,614 yards)

11-15 South Carolina winning 12-6 with not a single penalty called in 1902. Both schools suspended the series until 1909.

11-16 Frank Howard and Paul "Bear" Bryant, January 26th

11-17 Copyright after the 1981 National Championship football season

11-18 Hootie Ingram, won his last game against South Carolina and this made the entry issue even hotter!

11-19 False! No one ranked Clemson in the Top 20 pre-season

11-20 Nike

GROUP 12 QUESTIONS

12-1 What do these famous coaches, Frank Leahy, Joe Paterno, Woody Hayes, Urban Meyer, Nick Saban, Les Miles, Tom Osborne, and Barry Switzer all have in common?

12-2 What happened on September 24, 1966, at Memorial Stadium?

12-3 Which Head Football Coach with the second highest winningest percentage to only his mentor, Knute Rockne, has a career losing record against Clemson?

12-4 "The score is tied, and we're winning," comment was said by whom?

12-5 What is the Clemson theme song adopted by the Clemson football team?

12-6 When was the "Golden Age" of Clemson football?

12-7 Which player is in the College Football Hall of Fame, All Decade Team 1980s, All Century Team by *Sports Illustrated* in 2000?

12-8 When was the "Dark Ages" of Clemson football?

12-9 **T or F:** Clemson's record under Head Coach Danny Ford was 30-2-2 for the three years 1981-82-83.

12-10 What is the name of the student-produced Pep Rally (second largest in the country)?

12-11 Who is the all-time career leader for tackles for a loss?

12-12 With Clemson's win against Kentucky (39-35) in the Gator Bowl 2023, how long is the streak for consecutive years winning a post season game?

12-13 Which former Clemson Tiger had his football and basketball jersey retired?

12-14 Which season did Clemson win the ACC Coach of the Year, ACC Offensive and Defensive Player and Player of the Year, while Trevor Lawrence was Offensive Rookie of the year?

12-15 What winning feat did Head Coach Dabo Swinney accomplish in 2020?

12-16 Which Head Coach stated the famous quote, "Better to have died a small boy than fumble this football?"

12-17 Who had the ACC greatest game of returns, via interceptions and/or punt returns?

12-18 Which game did Head Coach Danny Ford "surprise" everyone when he had the team suit up for the first time wearing orange pants?

12-19 How many consecutive games did Hunter Renfrow have a reception?

12-20 In the 2022 season, what was Clemson's number so far for a 10-win season?

GROUP 12 ANSWERS

12-1 All have lost a Bowl Game to Clemson.

12-2 Howard's Rock was unveiled!

12-3 Frank Leahy, 0-1 against Clemson

12-4 Head Coach Frank Howard

12-5 Tiger Rag, a jazz standard, originally recorded and copyrighted by the original Dixieland Band in 1917.

12-6 1900-1903 coached by John Heisman (19-3-2 and winning percentage .833, still a record).

12-7 Terry Kinard, Clemson Ring of Honor Member.

12-8 1908 for 20 seasons; 69-82-10

12-9 True! Best in the nation!

12-10 "Tigerama" which started in 1957 and occurs the Friday night before Homecoming.

12-11 Michael Dean Perry, 61

12-12 13 years

12-13 Banks McFadden, 1995. Banks McFadden Building at Jervey Athletic Center dedicated in his honor.

12-14 Coach Dabo Swinney, Travis Etienne both Offensive and Player of the Year, and Celin Ferrell Defensive Player of the Year. 2018

12-15 "Double-Double Mission" a 10-win season for 10 straight seasons!

12-16 John Heisman, known for his Shakespearean prose.

12-17 Don Kelly, 223 yards; including 167 on punt returns and a 56-yard interception.

12-18 1980 vs. South Carolina, 27-6

12-19 Forty-three

12-20 19th season, Dabo Swinney with 10 so far.

 GROUP **13** QUESTIONS

13-1   How many Top-10 Teams did Clemson beat during their 1981 perfect season, National Championship?

13-2   What five famous Head Coaches were John Heisman's contemporaries?

13-3   What season was the first time ESPN College Game Day came to Clemson?

13-4   Before Head Coach Pell, how many years had Clemson not gone to a bowl game?

13-5   Which Head Coach played in three bowl games at Alabama and then four more as an assistant coach by 1978 when he coached in his first game in the Gator Bowl?

13-6   Which Head Coach had the greatest progress moving from eighth place to second place, the biggest improvement in ACC history?

13-7   Who was nicknamed, "Georgia Killer?"

13-8   Which season did Clemson rank No. 2 in Scoring Defense and No. 4 in Total Defense nationally?

13-9   Which coach coached at both South Carolina and Clemson?

13-10 Which game did Head Coach Dabo Swinney tie Head Coach Frank Howard for the most wins at Clemson?

13-11 Who was known as the "BEAR?"

13-12 What is the percentage for Head Coach Dabo Swinney with athletic eligibility players who earned a degree at Clemson?

13-13 Which Head Coach stated, "I want to coach a team that opponents don't look forward to playing?"

13-14 What was the first QB/RB duo selected in the common draft era from the same school in the first round?

13-15 Today, Riggs Field (second home football field) is now used for what activities?

13-16 Besides Trevor Lawrence, which other quarterback lead the team in passing yards for three seasons?

13-17 Which Head Coach won an away game and got married on the same day?

13-18 **T or F:** Clemson was the first team to go 15-0, winning a National Championship.

13-19 What are Clemson fans called?

13-20 Which team decided to stop playing football against Clemson in 1977?

GROUP 13 ANSWERS

13-1   Three: Georgia, Nebraska, and North Carolina

13-2   Zuppke (Illinois), Yost (Michigan), Stagg (Chicago), Wilce (Ohio State) and Bible (Texas A& M).

13-3   2006 vs. Georgia Tech

13-4   17 years before 1977, his first year of coaching.

13-5   Danny Ford

13-6   Head Coach Tommy Bowden, 1999

13-7   David Treadwell 2x kicking winning field goals for Clemson.

13-8   2017, also lead the ACC in the four major defensive categories (Scoring, Total, Rushing, Passing—a first in history!

13-9   Bob Williams, South Carolina 1902-1903, Clemson four terms 1906, 1909, 1913-1915, 1926.

13-10   Wake Forest, October 7, 2023, 17-12 at 165 wins. Record broken the following week.

13-11   An original Walk-On Guard Seth Penner, totaled 16 career games with 124 snaps.

13-12   98%, 350 out of 356! WOW!

13-13   Danny Ford

13-14   2021: QB Trevor Lawrence, RB Travis Etienne

13-15   Soccer Field and known as one of the best in the country.

13-16   Tajh Boyd, all three season greater than Trevor Lawrence, but Deshaun Watson did it twice with over 4,100+ yards each year.

13-17   John Heisman beating NC State and married Evelyn Barksdale, 1903

13-18   True! 2018

13-19   "Tater" because Clemson is an AG School

13-20   Georgia Tech! Clemson fans protested by adding the Tiger Paw stamp to $2 bills!

GROUP  14 QUESTIONS

14-1   Which Clemson Assistant Coach helped Will Shipley become the first player to earn First-Team All ACC Honors at three different positions?

14-2   Which Head Coach invented the hidden ball trick, which today is called the "Fumblerooski?"

14-3   Which Head Coach stated, "I ain't never going to apologize for a 21-point win over a state rival, ever?"

14-4   **T or F:** Head Coach Danny Ford would rather drive a pick-up truck instead of the Jaguar awarded to him.

14-5   Which end of Memorial Stadium do the players "Run Down the Hill?"

14-6   Which Dabo son was a redshirt freshman on the 2023 team?

14-7   Head Coach Dabo Swinney set the record for consecutive home wins at what number?

14-8   When was Clemson ranked for the first time by the Associated Press (AP)?

14-9   Who was Clemson's first two-time All-American?

14-10 Who is the career leader for pass interceptions?

14-11 Which Head Coach had some students masquerade as Clemson football players to party late into the night before the game?

14-12 What three Head Coaches graduated from Vanderbilt?

14-13 What is the "Tiger Pride" award celebrating?

14-14 **T or F:** Clemson has won 11 bowl games against coaches in the College Football Hall of Fame through 2023.

14-15 Through 2023, which quarterback has thrown the most touchdown passes in a season?

14-16 Four of Clemson's highest ranked wins came against which two teams?

14-17 What year did Clemson qualify for the Southern Intercollegiate Athletic Association (SIAA) Championship game?

14-18 Since 1906, which year did Clemson beat both Georgia and Georgia Tech at Death Valley?

14-19 Which game did Clemson go 12-12 third-down conversions, 536 yards rushing, 756 total yards, scoring 82 points?

14-20 Clemson's biggest rivalry is South Carolina, but what is the longest college football rivalry?

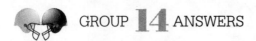 GROUP **14** ANSWERS

14-1 2021 College Football Hall of Fame Honoree C.J Spiller.

14-2 John Heisman

14-3 Head Coach Dabo Swinney

14-4 True!

14-5 East End of Death Valley

14-6 Clay Swinney

14-7 40, ended with a loss to South Carolina, 31-30, 2022

14-8 November 13, 1939, ended 12th in Final Poll

14-9 3 sports: Joe Blalock 1940-1941 in football

14-10 Terry Kinnard, 17, 1979-1982, also leader for takeaways with 19.

14-11 John Heisman to give his opponent, Georgia, the confidence of an easy win. Clemson won 44-5, 1902.

14-12 John Stone, Josh Cody, and Jess Neely

14-13 The Most Valuable Players at each position.

14-14 True! and in the future it will be at least 13 when Urban Meyer (Ohio State) and Nick Saban (Alabama) are inducted into the College Football Hall of Fame.

14-15 Deshaun Watson, 41, 2016

14-16 Alabama and THE Ohio State Buckeyes.

14-17 1903, 11-11 tie with Georgia Tech

14-18 1974

14-19 Wake Forest, 1981, 82 points still a record between two ACC teams.

14-20 Yale – Princeton, dating back to 1873!

GROUP 15 QUESTIONS

15-1   How many 100-yard kickoff returns did Derrick Hamilton have during his Clemson career?

15-2   How many different schools did Head Coach John Heisman coach?

15-3   Which Clemson Head Coach founded the National Football Coaches Association?

15-4   When he retired from coaching, he was one of five coaches with 150 wins, who was he?

15-5   Who was the Sports Information Director (SID) at Clemson for 24 years of his 40-year career?

15-6   What is the average number of fans per game at Memorial Stadium?

15-7   Who was the first Clemson player to be on a cover of *Sports Illustrated?*

15-8   Which Clemson Wide Receiver has won the Mackey Award?

15-9   Who lead the 1999 season with Tackles (186), Tackles for Loss (35) and Sacks at (16)?

15-10 What are the most conference wins Clemson has had in a season?

15-11 **T or F:** Head Coaches Pell, Ford, Bowden and Swinney have all been elected twice or more for the ACC Coach-of-the Year Award.

15-12 In the 2010s Dabo Swinney won 117 games which only trails Penn State (124 games won in the 1890s), but who beat Dabo's record during the same period?

15-13 What is the "Bone Sleeve?"

15-14 What was the largest winning margin over a Top-25 Team?

15-15 **T or F:** Clemson threw its first forward pass in history from a "trick" punt formation.

15-16 Which Clemson game had 36 future NFL players participate in the game?

15-17 Who made the tackle on Ohio State's QB Art Schlichter to prevent a two-point conversion in the 1978 Gator Bowl?

15-18 What Clemson tradition started in 1978, every time Clemson scores?

15-19 What is the best website for Clemson football fans by author's selection?

15-20 What is the First Friday Parade?

GROUP 15 ANSWERS

15-1   Two times: Maryland, 2001 and North Carolina, 2003

15-2   Seven: Auburn, Clemson, Georgia Tech, Pennsylvania, Washington& Jefferson, Rice and Oberlin

15-3   John Heisman

15-4   Frank Howard 1969, after 30 years as Head Coach (165-118-12)

15-5   Tim Bourret

15-6   78,000+ max, capacity is 81,500 but can accommodate 86,000 with standing room only.

15-7   Perry Tuttle Wide Receiver, 1981 Championship Team

15-8   Dwayne Allen, 2011

15-9   LB Keith Adams

15-10 Eight wins, 2018-19-20, 2022

15-11 True!

15-12 Alabama (124); Clemson won at least 12 games in five straight years 2015-2019, 69 games during this five-year period, the most in a five-year stretch in the AP poll era.

15-13 Each trombone player has an orange "Bone Sleeve" with purple stripes on the trombone slide.

15-14 45 points, over #22 Virginia, 2019 ACC Championship Game 62-17

15-15 True! 30-yard completion from punter Powell Lykes to George Warren.

15-16 1977 Clemson vs. Notre Dame, a 21-17 loss for Clemson. Seven players were first-round choices and players won 14 Super Bowl Championship rings.

15-17 Tackle Jim Stuckey – Clemson won 17-15.

15-18 The Tiger Mascot does push-ups after each score that equals the Clemson point total.

15-19 www.clemsontigers.com, other good websites www.tigernet.com and www.clemsonjunkies.com.

15-20 Since 1974, a Friday afternoon parade before the first home game.

 GROUP **16** QUESTIONS

16-1   What two Clemson players were named to the 40-man roster of Greatest Super Bowl Players released prior to Super Bowl XL?

16-2   Who said, "I finally retired for health reasons; the alumni were sick of me?"

16-3   Who coached in the first ever Division 1 coaching matchup of father and son?

16-4   Which Head Coach during his coaching career had 185 wins, 68 losses, and 18 ties?

16-5   2023 marks how many years has Clemson played football?

16-6   What is the title of the Clemson Yearbook?

16-7   Who said, "If you are going to give 110 percent, you can rub my rock. If you're not, keep your filthy hands off it?"

16-8   Which publication named Clemson the South's Best Tailgate?

16-9   **T or F:** Clemson once scored three times on punt returns vs Georgia.

16-10 Bubba Brown had 22 tackles in a single game twice in his career, who has had the most tackles in a single game?

16-11 Which Head Coach broke football into percentages; talent 25, mentality 20, aggressiveness 20, speed 20 and weight 15?

16-12 What was the name of the early conference Clemson played?

16-13 Who broke the Clemson home game winning record streak at 40 games?

16-14 What is the coldest and hottest temperature Clemson has played at kickoff?

16-15 Which two Head Coaches have won the Woody Hayes Award?

16-16 Who was the first player in any sport at Clemson to play professional ball?

16-17 What was the first time two Top-10 ACC teams met?

16-18 Who ranks first at Clemson with career kickoff return yards (2,052) and tied for number one in returns for touchdowns in the NCAA?

16-19 Which Head Coach personally delivers a postgame prayer, and will not tolerate cursing by his staff or his players?

16-20 Why did Clemson stop wearing purple jerseys until 1962 once again?

GROUP 16 ANSWERS

16-1 Charlie Waters and Jeff Bostic

16-2 Head Coach Frank Howard

16-3 Bobby Bowden, Florida State; and Tommy Bowden, Clemson. Florida State Seminoles won 17-14, in 1999.

16-4 John Heisman

16-5 128 Seasons

16-6 *Taps,* since 1908

16-7 Head Coach Frank Howard, September 23, 1967, beating Wake Forest 23-6, the Legend was started!

16-8 *Southern Living*

16-9 True! November 7, 1914; five times in a season (1948)

16-10 LB Keith Adams vs. South Carolina, 1999 with 27 tackles

16-11 John Heisman

16-12 Southern Intercollegiate Athletic Association (SIAA)

16-13 South Carolina, record ran from 2016 to 2022.

16-14 24 degrees vs. Auburn 1961, 95 degrees at Texas A & M 2004, Both losses!

16-15 Danny Ford 1981, Dabo Swinney, 2018

16-16 End Vet Sitton, but a pitcher who played for the Cleveland Indians.

16-17 1981, Clemson vs. North Carolina

16-18 C.J. Spiller (2006-2009)

16-19 Ken Hatfield

16-20 Purple made the players too hot! They now wear either white or orange.

 GROUP **17** QUESTIONS

17-1 In 2018, how many players had also received their degrees before playing the National Championship game?

17-2 Which Head Coach had a 31-13-1 record against 15 coaches now in the College Football Hall of Fame?

17-3 Who did Head Coach Frank Howard call his best player?

17-4 Which Head Coach was Captain of the baseball and football teams at Notre Dame?

17-5 What is the record for consecutive passes without an interception?

17-6 Who is the leading receiver with 100+ yard games?

17-7 By many, this 1979 upset victory on the road is considered one of the biggest wins in Clemson's history. Who was the team they defeated?

17-8 Who was Clemson's first, first-round NFL draft choice?

17-9 Which Clemson player was the first to win the "Academic Heisman Trophy," the William V. Campbell Trophy?

17-10 What was Clemson's greatest comeback win?

17-11 Who is the only Clemson graduate to become a Head Coach at Clemson?

17-12 Which Head Football Coach also had the highest winning percentage of any Clemson baseball coach?

17-13 Which kicker was unretired when Head Coach Dabo Swinney came calling for the Florida State game 2023?

17-14 What is Lover's Lane at Clemson?

17-15 Name the four Clemson players who have been inducted (so far) in the College Football Hall of Fame?

17-16 What span of years did Clemson have six consecutive ACC Titles?

17-17 **T or F:** So far, Clemson has 34 finishes in the Top-25 in the Modern Era (since 1968), and 59 times since 1939 in the AP and Coaches Poll.

17-18 Which ACC football stadium is the second largest continuous brick structure in the world?

17-19 **T or F:** Head Coach Frank Howard introduced the "East-Coast Formation."

17-20 Which team had a pre-season ranking of No.4 and one of the favorites to win the National Championship?

 GROUP **17** ANSWERS

17-1 26 players, including two with Master's Degrees.

17-2 Danny Ford

17-3 Fred Cone; Clemson Hall of Fame, South Carolina Hall of Fame, Green Bay Packer Hall of Fame, one hundred Year Anniversary Team, Clemson Ring of Honor.

17-4 Frank Shaughnessy

17-5 366 by Trevor Lawrence

17-6 Sammy Watkins, 15 games, 2011-13

17-7 Notre Dame, 1979, 16-10. It was only the third time in 40 years that Notre Dame lost its final home game.

17-8 Banks McFadden, 1939, Brooklyn Dodgers, also first Clemson player to compete in the College All-Star Game in Chicago.

17-9 Christian Wilkins also won a National Championship that same year, 2018.

17-10 28 points against Virginia, 1992

17-11 Shack Shealy, 1904

17-12 Coach John Heisman, three-year record 28-6-1 (.814)

17-13 Jonathan Weitz

17-14 A tradition, campus legend is that couples who walk hand-in-hand through the President's Park will marry.

17-15 Banks McFadden, Terry Kinard, Jeff Davis, C.J. Spiller.

17-16 2015-2020, the most consecutive outright titles by any ACC team.

17-17 True!

17-18 Florida State Doak Campbell Stadium, second to the Great Wall of China.

17-19 False! I made up the "East-Coast Formation," but Coach Howard did use the Single-Wing, T-Formation, and the I-Formation at various times in his coaching career at Clemson.

17-20 1988

GROUP 18 QUESTIONS

18-1 Which National Championship team has been honored in the Clemson Ring of Honor?

18-2 Which Quarterback had the most passing attempts, completions, passing yards and touchdowns in a career?

18-3 Who was Head Coach John Heisman's trainer at Oberlin in 1892?

18-4 Name the four players with interceptions in four consecutive games?

18-5 Which player was Captain of the 1981 National Championship team, All-American, ACC MVP and in College Football Hall of Fame?

18-6 What is the title of Head Coach Frank Howard's book?

18-7 Who stated, "Don't ever let them talk you into building a big stadium. Put about 10,000 seats behind the Y.M.C.A. That's all you'll ever need."

18-8 Who recorded 21 career touchdowns of at least 50 yards and an ACC record eight kick returns for touchdowns?

18-9 **T or F:** Clemson's all-time record through 2022 against ranked opponents is positive.

18-10 Which two 1980s Heisman Trophy winners never scored a touchdown against Clemson?

18-11 What year was the first Military Appreciation Game at Clemson?

18-12 In which 2023 game did Head Coach Dabo Swinney state, "It's almost indescribable what I just saw?"

18-13 Which season did the Clemson-Ohio State TV viewership out-do the National Championship game?

18-14 What is the all-time record for three defending National Champions visiting Memorial Stadium?

18-15 Which Clemson Head Coach holds the record at Notre Dame for the longest fumble return for a touchdown?

18-16 What is the record for kicking consecutively made extra points?

18-17 **T or F:** Deshaun Watson completed passes for over 4,000+ yards in back-to-back seasons.

18-18 Which Head Coach beat three nationally ranked teams in a row, a first for any ACC team?

18-19 Which game did Clemson give up 35 points in a quarter, 49 in a half and 70 for the game?

18-20 Who kicked a 37-yard field goal as time expired to win 25-24 vs. KSU and clinch Clemson's second 11-win season?

GROUP 18 ANSWERS

18-1 1981 Championship Team

18-2 Tajh Boyd

18-3 Clarence Hemingway, father of Author Ernest Hemingway

18-4 Bobby Gage, Terry Kinard, Dexter Davis, Rashard Hall

18-5 Jeff Davis

18-6 The Clemson Legend, *Howard*

18-7 Head Coach Jess Neely as he left to coach Rice.

18-8 C.J. Spiller, 2006-2009

18-9 False! All-Time: 98 wins – 123 loses and two ties. All Competition: 798-472-45

18-10 Herschel Walker and George Rogers

18-11 1994, vs. Georgia Tech, with a fly-over of four F-16s from Shaw Air Force Base.

18-12 Loss to Duke 28-7. Clemson stumbled through four drives inside the Red Zone that ended without any points. Two missed field goals and two fumbles.

18-13 2020 Semifinal Game

18-14 0-3!

18-15 Coach Frank Shaughnessy, 107 yards against Kansas. Coached Clemson one season (4-4) and left to play baseball on Connie Macks Philadelphia Athletics.

18-16 122 by B.T. Potter

18-17 True! 2015 (4,104), 2016 (4,593)

18-18 Dabo Swinney, #21 Auburn, #11 FSU, #11 Virginia Tech in 2011.

18-19 2012 Orange Bowl vs. West Virginia, 70-33, all-time record for bowl games.

18-20 Chandler Catanzaro

 GROUP **19** QUESTIONS

19-1   When Clemson went 15-0 in 2008 to win the National Championship, how many of the teams they beat finished with a winning record?

19-2   What three conferences has Clemson been a part of over time?

19-3   What is the best Clemson football win?

19-4   What famous statement was made between Head Coach Frank Howard and IPTAY Executive Secretary Gene Willimon?

19-5   Jerry Richardson, owner of the Carolina Panthers, chose Memorial Stadium to play their games in their inaugural season. What was the year?

19-6   Which Clemson Head Coach was a three time All-American at Vanderbilt?

19-7   Who were the two ABC Commentators for the 1978 Gator Bowl vs. THE Ohio State Buckeyes?

19-8   What do Head Coaches Josh Cody and E.J. Stewart have in common outside of Clemson football?

19-9   **T or F:** Head Coach Dabo Swinney is the fourth Head Coach at the time to win 100 games in their first 10 years.

19-10 **T or F:** Clemson is undefeated all-time against eight of the winningest programs in major college football history.

19-11 Who was the first Tiger to be drafted No. 1 overall in the NFL Draft?

19-12 What was the famous "Pendleton Escapade?"

19-13 Who was Clemson's first three-time All American?

19-14 Which season had seven different teams ranked No. 1: the most in college football history?

19-15 What was the first time the two previous National Champions met during the regular season?

19-16 Name the four Clemson Head Coaches so far (2023) inducted into the College Football Hall of Fame.

19-17 What is the name of the field in Memorial Stadium?

19-18 The first Top-10 meeting between Clemson No. 4 and South Carolina No.9 in 2013 was won by which team?

19-19 In 2014 Clemson Defense was ranked No. 1, who was the Defensive Coordinator?

19-20 Who was the first player in history to amass over 4,000 yards passing and 1,000 yards rushing in a season?

GROUP 19 ANSWERS

19-1 12

19-2 Independent, Southern Association and Atlantic Coast Conference (ACC)

19-3 This question is meant to start friendly arguments! This author feels it was the very first game Clemson played in 1896, winning 14-6 over Furman. It was the first time many of the Clemson players saw a full-sized football field!

19-4 "Take this rock and throw it over the fence, or out in the ditch. Do something to get it out of my office."

19-5 1995, Season record 7-9, for the 29th NFL Team

19-6 Josh Cody, 1915-16 & 1919, selected as an All-Time All-American by the Football Writers Association. He also played basketball, baseball and ran track as a Commodore.

19-7 Ara Parseghian and Keith Jackson. They never mention the incident with Coach Woody Hayes.

19-8 Both fought in World War I.

19-9 True!

19-10 False! But they are 12-4 against the THE Ohio State University, Alabama, Oklahoma, Penn State, Nebraska, and Notre Dame.

19-11 Trevor Lawrence, by Jacksonville Jaguars 2021.

19-12 Aprils Fool's Day 1908, 306 Clemson Cadets removed the Civil War cannon from the Pendleton Town Square and brought it back to Clemson. All 306 were expelled! 19 years following the prank Clemson's record was 69-82-10, .460 winning percentage. OUCH!

19-13 "The Refrigerator" William Perry

19-14 1981

19-15 1982 Georgia vs. Clemson. Georgia won 13-7.

19-16 John Heisman, Jess Neely, Frank Howard, and Danny Ford

19-17 Frank Howard Field, 1974

19-18 South Carolina 31-17, fifth straight loss to South Carolina

19-19 Brent Venables, now Head Coach at the University of Oklahoma.

19-20 Deshaun Watson, 2016

GROUP 20 QUESTIONS

20-1 Who did Clemson beat and by what score to win the 1981 National Championship?

20-2 Which Clemson Head Coach played for the Alabama Crimson Tide in three bowl games?

20-3 Who convinced the Football Rules Committee to legalize the forward pass?

20-4 Through the 2023 season, how many Clemson players in history have been drafted?

20-5 Who stated, "The rock has strange powers. When you rub it, and run down the hill, the adrenaline flows. It is the most emotional experience I have, ever had?"

20-6 What was the name of the first bowl game Clemson played in?

20-7 What are the jersey numbers of the three retired football numbers?

20-8 Who holds the record for the most yards receiving in a single game?

20-9 Which Clemson Tiger was an All-American in football and basketball in the same year?

20-10 Which team has eight players in the Clemson Hall of Fame?

20-11 Head Coach Charlie Pell played for Alabama Head Coach Bear Bryant and in his first season played another coach, who also played at Alabama. Who was the other coach and what was his team?

20-12 Who won the MVP award in the 1986 Gator Bowl and the 1988 Citrus Bowl?

20-13 Who was the first Clemson running back to rush for over 2,000 yards in his career?

20-14 Joe Paterno, Penn State Head Coach, worst margin of defeat occurred in which bowl game against Clemson?

20-15 **T or F:** Head Coach Danny Ford's record between 1981-83 was college football's best record.

20-16 How many kick returns did Clemson have without a return for a touchdown via a punt or kickoff, until one each against Georgia Tech in 1987?

20-17 Quarterback Tajh Boyd threw for five touchdowns and totaled 505 yards against whom to win the 2014 orange Bowl?

20-18 What season did Clemson end up ranked in the Top 4 for the fifth straight year?

20-19 Who became the first Clemson player with three touchdown receptions against the South Carolina Gamecocks?

20-20 How many National Coaching Awards through 2023 has Head Coach Dabo Swinney won?

GROUP 20 ANSWERS

20-1 Nebraska 22-15 in the Orange Bowl

20-2 Danny Ford

20-3 John Heisman

20-4 293

20-5 Michael Dean Perry

20-6 "Championship of the South" 1903, Playing to an 11-11 tie.

20-7 #4 Steve Fuller, #28 C.J. Spiller and #66 Banks McFadden

20-8 Sammy Watkins, vs. THE Ohio State Buckeyes, 16 receptions for 227 yards and he is also tied for second with 202 yards vs. Wake Forest.

20-9 Banks McFadden (1939)

20-10 1948, was a perfect record of 11-0.

20-11 Jackie Sherrill, Pittsburgh Panthers #10 & Clemson #11, Pittsburgh won 34-3.

20-12 Rodney Williams

20-13 Fred Cone, 1948-1950, also in the Packer Hall of Fame and Clemson Ring of Honor.

20-14 1988, Florida Citrus Bowl 35-10

20-15 True! 30-2-2

20-16 999 Returns!

20-17 THE Ohio State Buckeyes #7 40-35, 11-2 season for Clemson.

20-18 2019, also the one loss broke the 29-game winning streak.

20-19 Mike Williams

20-20 Ten different ones!

GROUP 21 QUESTIONS

21-1 **T or F:** When Clemson beat Ohio State 31-0 it was the first shut out for Ohio State in 23 years and Head Coach Urban Meyer.

21-2 Who took over the head coaching position after Head Coach Danny Ford resigned?

21-3 Who has been inducted into the College Sports Information Directors of American (SIDA) Hall of Fame from Clemson?

21-4 What does the trademark BYOG mean?

21-5 When did Clemson win its first State Championship?

21-6 How many games in 1981 were played before a rushing touchdown was given up by the Clemson defense?

21-7 **T or F:** Clemson's record against all FBS Conferences is positive.

21-8 What is the longest scoring play in history by Clemson?

21-9 What is the name of the award for the most solid, consistent, and dependable player at each position?

21-10 What game did Head Coach Dabo Swinney become the all-time winningest Head Coach at Clemson?

21-11 Which National Championship season did Clemson play the toughest schedule beating six teams that finished in the Top 25 teams by Associated Press (AP)?

21-12 Through the 2023 season, Clemson has finished in the Top 20 Home Attendance at "Death Valley". How many straight seasons?

21-13 Who has won the Bill Willis Award 2017 for Defensive Lineman of the Year from the Touchdown Club of Columbus?

21-14 Which Clemson Head Coach also served as a Volunteer Fireman?

21-15 Who won the first meeting of two 8-0 ACC teams, North Carolina, and Clemson for the ACC Championship game in 2015?

21-16 Who was the only player to return a punt for a touchdown in Chris Gardocki's career at Clemson?

21-17 When did Clemson beat three ranked teams in the month of September becoming the first team in college football history to perform this feat?

21-18 What year did Florida State join the ACC?

21-19 Who are Clemson's only two-time Consensus All-Americans through 2023?

21-20 **T or F:** Clemson has an all-time winning record against all current ACC teams.

 GROUP **21** ANSWERS

21-1 True! Aka "Baskin-Robbins" Game

21-2 Ken Hatfield, former Arkansas Head Coach

21-3 Tim Bourret, Bob Bradley, Joe Sherman

21-4 "Bring Your Own Guts" created by Head Coach Dabo Swinney after Notre Dame game in 2015.

21-5 1897, Beat South Carolina 18-6

21-6 Six games

21-7 True! But not against conference USA (7-7), Mid-American (5-5) and Mountain West (2-2).

21-8 A missed field goal returned 108 yards vs. Georgia (13-31) in 1968.

21-9 Solid Rock Award

21-10 Beat Notre Dame 31-23, for the 166th victory, breaking his tie with Frank Howard of 11-4-23.

21-11 2016, 14-1 beating #3 Louisville, #2 THE Ohio State University and #1 Alabama

21-12 43 seasons and should continue.

21-13 Christian Wilkins, 2017, also won the Jim Tatum Award for Top Scholar in the ACC and the Campbell Award for Academics.

21-14 Frank Howard

21-15 Clemson winning 45-37.

21-16 Deion Sanders, FSU, NFL Player with the Dallas Cowboys, and a college Head Coach now at Colorado as of 2024.

21-17 2017: Auburn, Boston College, Virginia Tech

21-18 1992, with the first league game against Clemson, winning 24-20.

21-19 Terry Kinard 1981-1982, Vic Beasley 2014-2015

21-20 False! All-Time losing records against FSU, Georgia Tech, Pittsburgh, and most wins against Wake Forest.

 GROUP **22** QUESTIONS

22-1   Which Head Coach was born in Barlow Bend, Alabama?

22-2   Which Head Coach stated, "I want players to think as positively as an 85-year-old man who married a 25-year-old woman and bought a five-bedroom house next to the elementary school?"

22-3   What position did Frank Howard play at Alabama?

22-4   **T or F:** In the 1980s Clemson had the highest winning percentage.

22-5   What was one of Head Coach Danny Ford's coaching skills he was known for?

22-6   What year did Clemson defeat 12 FBS schools that finished with a winning record, including five that totaled 10+ wins and six that finished in the Top 25 of the AP Poll?

22-7   What two coaches have won the Woody Hayes Trophy?

22-8   Which season did Clemson have 11 games where they never trailed?

22-9   What did Center Kyle Young and Linebacker Chad Carson have in common?

22-10   Which Clemson receiver had 166 receptions for 2,498 yards with back-to-back 1,000-yard seasons?

22-11   Which Ring of Honor member never played high school football?

22-12   How many times has Head Coach Dabo Swinney won the Bear Bryant Award through 2023?

22-13   What two Clemson Head Coaches won their Conference Championship in their first year of coaching?

22-14   After AD Bobby Robinson would not extend Ken Hatfield's contract, Hatfield stated, "This is not a termination, this not a resignation, this is a separation." Where did Hatfield coach next?

22-15   Who did Clemson play in its first overtime game?

22-16   Which Head Coach coached a team he had not watched during the regular season going into a bowl game?

22-17   Who holds the rushing record for a freshman running back against rival South Carolina with 27 carries for 191 yards?

22-18   How many times did Head Coach Tommy Bowden lose to his father Bobby Bowden before he finally beat No. 3 Florida State?

22-19   Head Coach Tommy Bowden beat Head Coach Lou Holtz from South Carolina in 2000+ with a winning field goal with three seconds remaining, kicked by whom?

22-20   Who stated it was ironic that two coaches ended their careers for "getting into a fight at a Clemson game?"

GROUP 22 ANSWERS

22-1 Frank Howard

22-2 Charley Pell

22-3 Guard

22-4 False! Fifth best percentage, but won three consecutive ACC Titles, 1986-1987-1988.

22-5 Danny Ford let his Assistant Coaches coach their position(s)!

22-6 2016 National Champions

22-7 Danny Ford (1981), Dabo Swinney (2018)

22-8 2019

22-9 Both are Academic All-Americans 1999, 2000, 2001

22-10 Rod Gardner

22-11 Fred Cone, Coach Frank Howard stated, "The best, if not the best, football player I ever had!"

22-12 Three times 2015-2016-2018

22-13 John Heisman (1900) and Frank Howard (1940)

22-14 Rice University until he retired in 2005.

22-15 Duke, 1997, winning 29-20.

22-16 Tommy West, 1993, winning the Peach Bowl over Kentucky 14-13.

22-17 Wayne Gallman, winning 35-17, 2014.

22-18 Four times, winning the fifth game 26-10, 2003.

22-19 Freshman Aaron Hunt,16-14

22-20 Lou Holtz, South Carolina Coach, and reference to Woody Hayes

GROUP **23** QUESTIONS

23-1 **T or F:** When Head Coach Dabo Swinney beat Oklahoma 37-17 in 2015, the victory gave him a bowl win over a Top 25 team led by a coach who already had a National Championship for the fourth consecutive year — a first in college football.

23-2 What was the win/loss record of the "Bowden" bowl games?

23-3 Who coached three bowl game wins by a total score of five points?

23-4 Which season is remembered for setting the most records?

23-5 "Horny-Handed sons of toil" was an expression of which Clemson supporter in the background?

23-6 Cryotherapy, Photobiomodulation, Hyperbaric, and Sensory Deprivation are all words describing what facility at Clemson?

23-7 Which college opened with Clemson 39 years with a record of 24 shutouts in 39 games, with three wins and four ties?

23-8 Who holds the ACC single season and career records for all-purpose yards of 2,680 one season and 7,588 career (second most in FBS history at the time of his graduation)?

23-9 Who was the first running back to score on a 90-yard run?

23-10 Which two Clemson Head Coaches won the Frank Broyles Award back-to-back years for the first time ever for two different coaches from the same school.?

23-11 When was "Howard's Rock" unveiled for the first game?

23-12 What two players joined Head Coach Frank Howard as Charter Members of the Clemson Athletic Hall of Fame?

23-13 Which kicker set or tied nine NCAA records for field goals and scoring?

23-14 Which two Clemson players have won the Archie Griffin Award?

23-15 Which quarterback established an ACC record of four passing touchdowns to four different receivers and rushed for 184 yards and two touchdowns?

23-16 Who was Woody Dantzler's "Go-to Receiver?"

23-17 Who were Clemson's "Thunder and Lightning?"

23-18 Which quarterback was the one to beat South Carolina four straight years?

23-19 Which two wide receivers blocked a punt and scored a touchdown vs. South Carolina in 2007?

23-20 Who instituted a "Tiger Walk" upon the team's arrival at Memorial Stadium?

GROUP **23** ANSWERS

23-1 True!

23-2 Nine Bowden Bowls, Bobby winning five; Tommy winning four of the last five games.

23-3 Frank Howard, 1940 Cotton Bowl, 1949 Gator Bowl and 1951 Orange Bowl.

23-4 1999 under Coach Bowden, 38 records, 26 on Offense

23-5 Governor of South Carolina, Ben Tillman aka "Pitchfork Ben."

23-6 100 Yards of Wellness Center

23-7 Presbyterian College, Late Head Coach Lonnie McMillian called Clemson "Death Valley" at Memorial Stadium.

23-8 C.J. Spiller, 2009, and 2006-2009

23-9 Banks McFadden, 1939 vs. Presbyterian College, followed by Buck George, 1951 and Travis Etienne 2019.

23-10 Brent Venables 2016, Tony Elliott 2017

23-11 September 24, 1966, against Virginia. Clemson trailed by 18 points with 17 minutes left, but the Tigers came back to win 40-35 on a 75-yard touchdown pass.

23-12 Joe Blalock and Banks McFadden

23-13 Obed Ariri (1977-1980) 63 career field goals

23-14 Deshaun Watson (2015) Trevor Lawrence (2018)

23-15 Woody Dantzler 2001 – Clemson 45, North Carolina State 37

23-16 Rod Gardner

23-17 James Davis and C.J. Spiller. ESPN used it for the first time on College Game Day in 2006.

23-18 Charlie Whitehurst

23-19 La' Donte Harris and Nelson Faerber.

23-20 Dabo Swinney 2008 Georgia Tech

GROUP 24 QUESTIONS

24-1 Who were the two Charter Member football players inducted into the Clemson Ring of Honor, 1994?

24-2 Who originated the center snap and the "Hike" or "Hep" count signals shouted by the quarterback?

24-3 **T or F:** The SEC has a greater winning percentage in bowl games than the ACC.

24-4 Who taught Head Coach Danny Ford the following "We" win as a team, but "I" lose as a coach?"

24-5 Who was responsible for putting the Clemson name among the annuals of the great early collegiate teams?

24-6 What is the name of the award for outstanding play, academic excellence, and community service?

24-7 Who stated, "Continue to do things in an uncommon way, continue to be 'All-In!' Continue to be a person of excellence in everything you do?"

24-8 Which Clemson quarterback has won the Davey O'Brien Award twice?

24-9 During the decade of the 1940s how many running backs ran for 200 yards or more in a game?

24-10 Which kicker was 43-of-43 extra points and kicked a 50-yard plus field goal each of his four seasons?

24-11 Which out-going coach was carried off the field after beating South Carolina 28-19?

24-12 Who was the first Clemson player to have a 50-yard rushing and receiving touchdown in the same game?

24-13 Why is January 15, 2009, a key date in Clemson football?

24-14 Which team did Clemson beat twice in the same year, 2011, for the first time in history?

24-15 Who set a Clemson record against THE Ohio State Buckeyes with 227 receiver yards with 16 receptions in the Orange Bowl?

24-16 **T or F:** Clemson was the first non-SEC team to win consecutive games against Top 10 SEC teams.

24-17 Which major bowl game did Clemson Quarterback Tajh Boyd set record numbers of over 500 yards total yardage?

24-18 Who is now next for Head Coach Dabo Swinney to pass for career ACC victories?

24-19 Who was Will Shipley's position coach to become the first player in ACC history with the First Team All-Conference Honor at three distinct positions?

24-20 Who is the highest NFL pick after Banks McFadden?

GROUP 24 ANSWERS

24-1 Steve Fuller, and Banks McFadden

24-2 John Heisman

24-3 False! ACC, with a winning percentage greater than 50%, leads all conferences.

24-4 Bear Bryant, Alabama coach for Danny Ford, all SEC selection as an offensive tackle in 1969.

24-5 Coach John Heisman 1900-1903

24-6 The PAW Award

24-7 Head Coach Dabo Swinney

24-8 Deshaun Watson, 2015, 2016; Also, the Chic Harley Award for the Nation's Top Player.

24-9 None! Best record was Butch Butler, 192 yards.

24-10 Donald Igwebuike (1981-1984)

24-11 Tommy West

24-12 C.J. Spiller; 2006 vs. Georgia Tech

24-13 C.J. Spiller stated he would play his Senior Year 2009 at Clemson! It changed Clemson football forever!

24-14 Virginia Tech

24-15 Sammy Watkins, Clemson won 40-35.

24-16 True! Last game 2012 LSU, and first game 2013 Georgia

24-17 Orange Bowl 2014, 31-40 passing, 376 yards and five touchdowns, 127 yards rushing vs. THE Ohio State Buckeyes.

24-18 Bobby Bowden, Florida State University

24-19 C.J. Spiller, three positions: Running Back, All-Purpose and Specialist.

24-20 Trevor Lawrence 2021

GROUP 25 QUESTIONS

25-1   Which Head Coach was been called "The Father of Clemson Football?"

25-2   Where is the College Football Hall of Fame located?

25-3   Who stated, "The Paw is flying on top of that mountain tonight?"

25-4   What was the penalty for Clemson set down by the NCAA for recruiting violations 1982?

25-5   Who set the initial record of four straight wins over South Carolina?

25-6   **T or F:** Clemson was just the sixth National Champion to play the nation's most difficult schedule (2016 season) when they won it all.

25-7   Which Clemson player has won the ACC Player-of-the-Week nine times?

25-8   Which Clemson freshman receiver caught seven passes for 185 yards and two touchdowns against South Carolina, winning 35-17, 2014?

25-9   Who had 10 consecutive games with a touchdown reception?

25-10 What school, other than Clemson, had more officers in World War II among its graduates?

25-11 **T or F:** Clemson has never lost a game where they ran for two hundred yards and passed for two hundred yards.

25-12 **T or F:** Head Coach Charlie Pell took a program from five wins in 1975-76 to a record of 18-4-1 two years later.

25-13 Who was the first walk-on to earn All-American Honors?

25-14 Who was drafted ninth overall, was a Unanimous All-American and graduated in December 2009 before the Bowl Game?

25-15 Who threw six touchdown passes in his first career start as a freshman?

25-16 **T or F:** Travis Etienne averaged over seven yards plus per carry for three seasons.

25-17 Who did Clemson beat for the first ever to win over a Top 10 team in Death Valley?

25-18 Who won the Mackey Award as the Nation's top Tight End?

25-19 Swinney became the sixth fastest coach in FBS history and fourth fastest in the Modern Era to register 150 career victories. 14 of the 16 coaches who accomplished this feat are in the College Football Hall of Fame. Name the other two.

25-20 **T or F:** Clemson has had three 100+ yard rushers in a single game.

GROUP 25 ANSWERS

25-1 Walter Riggs, First Coach 1896 and 1999. The coaching record was 6-3.

25-2 250 Marietta Street, NW, Atlanta, GA 30313. www.cfbhall.com

25-3 Head Coach Frank Howard

25-4 Barred from Bowl Games 1982-1983, NO! TV 1983-1984

25-5 "Big Man" Josh Cody, in fact, never lost to South Carolina Gamecocks.

25-6 True!

25-7 Tajh Boyd

25-8 Artavis Scott

25-9 Deandre Hopkins

25-10 Texas A & M, 1943 the U.S. Military drafted all of Clemson's entire Junior and Senior classes.

25-11 False! Lost at Duke 28-7 in 2023

25-12 True! Then took the Florida job and Danny Ford became the new Head Coach

25-13 Greg Huegel (2015-2018) 27 field goals in 2015 and 217 extra points — both records at the time.

25-14 C.J. Spiller

25-15 Five-Star QB Deshaun Watson vs. North Carolina.

25-16 True!

25-17 North Carolina State #10, 1967 aka "The Orange Shoe Game"

25-18 Dwayne Allen (2011), Jordan Leggett was twice a finalist.

25-19 Urban Meyer, which he and Dabo are not eligible for yet!

25-20 True! Seven times so far and more to come!

GAME DAY WEATHER FORECAST

"Death Valley" Memorial Stadium
Clemson University
Longitude 82.8433 | Latitude 34.6788

Memorial Stadium Forecast
https://forecast.weather.gov/MapClick.php?lon=82.84338569431566&lat=34.67887723600134

Radar
https://radar.weather.gov/station/kgsp/standard

Satellite
https://www.star.nesdis.noaa.gov/GOES/conus_brand.php?sat=G16&band=GEOCOLOR&length=24

Hourly Weather Graph
https://forecast.weather.gov/MapClick.php?lat=34.6789&=-82.8434&unit=0&lg=english&FcstType=graphical

Weather Model
www.tropicaltidbits.com

Wind Conditions
www.Windy.com

The ROAR
The official flagship stations for Clemson football

WCCP FM   105.5
WAHT (AM)   97.5

NATIONAL COLLEGE FOOTBALL AWARDS

The National College Football Awards Association (NCFAA) was founded in 1997 as a coalition of major United States college football awards. The stated purpose of the NCFAA is to protect, preserve and enhance the integrity, influence, and prestige of college football's various awards. The NCFAA also encourages professionalism and the highest stands possible for the administration of college football awards and the selection of their winners. The 25 awards are considered among the most prestigious in college football.

- Bronko Nagurski Trophy (Defensive Player)
- Broyles Award (Assistant Coach)
- Burlsworth Trophy (Player who began his career as a walk-on)
- Butkus Award (Linebacker)
- Chuck Bednarik Award (Defensive Player)
- Davey O'Brien Award (Quarterback)
- Disney Spirit Award (Inspirational Player, Team or Figure)
- Doak Walker Award (Running Back)
- Eddie Robinson Award (National Coach of the Year)
- Fred Biletnikoff Award (Receiver)
- George Munger Award (Head Coach)
- Heisman Trophy (Outstanding Player)
- John Mackey Award (Tight End)
- Lou Groza Award (Place-Kicker)
- Maxwell Award (Best Player)
- NCFAA Contributions Award (Exceptional Contributions to CFB)
- Outland Trophy (Interior Lineman)
- Paul Horning Award (Most Versatile)
- Paycom Jim Thrope Award (Defensive Back)
- Ray Guy Award (Punter)
- Rimington Trophy (Center)
- Stallings Award (Humanitarian Coach)
- Uplifting Athletes (Player impacting rare disease research)
- Walter Camp Award (Player of the Year)
- William V. Campbell Trophy (Scholar-athlete, "Academic Heisman")
- Wuerffel Trophy (Exemplary community service)

COLLEGE FOOTBALL AWARDS

Additional College Football Awards from private organizations, clubs, and businesses.

- Academic All-America Team Members of the Year
- AT&T ESPN All-America Player
- Eddie Robinson Award (FCS Coach of the Year)
- ESPY All-America Player
- The Home Depot (Coach of the Year)
- Johnny Unitas Golden Arm Award (Outstanding Senior QB)
- Lombardi Award (Nation's Top Player)
- Lott IMPACT Trophy (Outstanding Defensive Player)
- NAIA Football Player of the Year
- Senior CLASS Award Football Winners
- Sporting News College Football Player of the Year
- STATS FCS Defensive Player of the Year
- STATS FCS Freshman Player of the Year
- STATS FCS Offensive Player of the Year
- Ted Hendricks (Defensive End of the Year Award)
- UPI College Football Player of the Year
- UPI Lineman of the Year

COLLEGE FOOTBALL NATIONAL PLAYER AWARDS

- Associated Press College Football Player of the Year
- Buck Buchanan Award
- Deacon Jones Trophy
- Fred Mitchell Outstanding Place Kicker Award
- Gagliardi Trophy
- Gene Upshaw Award
- Harlon Hill Trophy
- Jerry Rice Award
- Jet Award
- Joe Moore Award
- Lombardi Award
- Manning Award
- Melberger Award
- Patrick Mannelly Award
- Peter Mortell Holder of the Year Award
- Polynesian Football Player of the Year Award
- Rudy Awards
- Ted Hendricks Award

PAUL "BEAR" BRYANT AWARDS

- Coach of the Year
- Conference Coach of the Year
- Fan Vote Favorite Award
- Heart of a Champion Award
- Lifetime Achievement Award
- Newcomer Coach of the Year

TOUCHDOWN CLUB OF COLUMBUS

- Archie Griffin Award (College MVP Player for the entire season)
- Bill Willis Trophy (Top Collegiate Defensive Lineman)
- Chic Harley Award (College Football Player of the Year)
- Freshman of the Year (Top College Football Newcomer)
- Jack Lambert Trophy (Top Collegiate Linebacker)
- Jack Tatum Trophy (Top Collegiate Defensive Back)
- Jim Brown Trophy (NCAA's Top Running Back)
- Jim Parker Trophy (Top Collegiate Offensive Lineman)
- Kellen Moore Award (Quarterback of the Year Award)
- Ozzie Newsome Award (Top Collegiate Tight End)
- Paul Warfield Trophy (Nation's Top Collegiate Wide Receiver)
- Sammy Baugh Trophy (Nation's Top Passer)
- Valde Award (Most Accurate College Football Kicker)
- Woody Hayes Trophy (Top Collegiate Coach)
- Zuppke Award (Touchdown Club of Columbus's selection of National Champion)

CLEMSON FOOTBALL BOOKS

Following is a list of Clemson football books to increase your knowledge and understanding of the great traditions and games of Clemson Tigers Football.

100 Things Clemson Fans Should Know & Do Before They Die
Lou Sahadi

Dabo's World: The Life and Career of Coach Swinney and the Rise of Clemson Football
Lars Anderson

CLEMSON: Where the Tigers Play
Sam Blackman

If These Walls Could Talk: Clemson Tigers: Stories from the Clemson Tigers Sideline, Locker Room, and Press Box
Tim Bourret, Dabo Swinney, and Sam Blackman

Hidden History of Clemson Football
Will Vandervort

The Clemson Legend HOWARD
Frank Howard

Tales from CLEMSON'S 1981 Championship Season
Ken Tysiac

CLEMSON TOUGH: Guts and Glory Under Dabo Swinney
Larry Williams and Zachary Hanby

RETURN TO GLORY: The story of Clemson's Historic 2015 Season
The Greenville News

CLEMSON Adult Coloring Book
Darl Hall

DABO SWINNEY: Bring Your Own Guts
Jackson Carter

CLEMSON FOOTBALL BOOKS (continued)

TOP of the HILL: Dabo Swinney and Clemson's Rise to College Football Greatness
Manie Robinson and Tajh Boyd

DABO'S DYNASTY: Clemson's Rise to College Football Supremacy
Larry Williams

CLEMSON: Where the Tigers Play
Sam Blackman, Bob Bradley, Chuck Kriese, and Will Vandervort

Clemson Through the Eyes of the Tiger
John Seketa and the Clemson Mascots

Clemson: All In Team™ Foundation 500 Memorable Football Trivia Q & A
Mike McGuire

Clemson Football Vault: The Story of the Tigers
Tim Bourret

TIGER RAG! History of Clemson Tigers Football
Steve's Football Bible, LLC

CLEMSON TIGERS: Inside College Football
Leah Kaminski

Classic Clashes of the Carolina-Clemson Football Rivalry: A State of Diunion
Travis Haney

Daily Devotions for Die-Hard Fans Clemson Tigers
Ed McMinn

UNTAMED: Clemson's Dominant Path to the National Championship
The Greenville News

The Danny Ford Years at Clemson: Romping and Stomping
Larry Williams

Clemson University: 2016 National Champions
Tim Bourret

CLEMSON FOOTBALL BOOKS (continued)

Death Valley Days: The Glory of Clemson Football
Bob Bradley

DABO: A Novel Inspired by the Life of William Christopher Swinney
J. T. Leary

Clemson University Football Bible Verses
Craig Copeland

CLEMSON CROWNED
The Greenville News

Find the Tiger at Clemson: A Seek and Find Adventure Book
for Clemson University Fans
Samantha Hawthorne

Clemson Tigers Football Fun Facts
Trivia Ape

EARNING THE STRIPES: Clemson's 2015 Historic Football Season
Independent Mail

A Football History: Clemson Tigers
The Washington Post

Goodnight Clemson: Tigers Bedtime Story
Samantha Hawthorne

I HATE CLEMSON: 303 Reasons Why You Should Too
Paul Finebaum

Great Coaches in Clemson Tigers Football
Brian Kelly

Carolina vs. Clemson — Clemson vs. Carolina: A Century of Unparalleled
Rivalry in College Football
John Chandler Griffin

CLEMSON FOOTBALL BOOKS (continued)

Clemson Football '89
Tim Bourret

Great Moments in Clemson Tigers Football
Brian Kelly

Fighting Like Cats and Dogs
Kyle King

Great Players in Clemson Tigers Football
Brian Kelly

My Daddy Loves CLEMSON Football
Michael Shoule, Gus Katsanevakis & Sara Lucas

A History of Clemson Football
Joe Sherman

Trevor Lawrence: Tigers & Triumph
Bailey Garza

CLEMSON FOOTBALL: Inside the Tiger's Lair: A Biography
Melissa B. Quintana

DEATH VALLEY: 72 Years of Exciting Football at Clemson University
Johnny Martin

Dueling Dynasties: How Clemson and Alabama dominated College Football
John Crowley